SCHOL

Data Handling

Year 2

Book End, Range Road, Witney, Oxfordshire, OX29 0YD
www.scholastic.co.uk

© 2011, Scholastic Ltd

1 2 3 4 5 6 7 8 9   1 2 3 4 5 6 7 8 9 0

British Library Cataloguing-in-Publication Data
A catalogue record for this book is available from the British Library.

ISBN 978-1407-12520-6
Printed by Bell & Bain
CD duplicated by Media Plant

Text © 2011 Ann Montague-Smith and Julia Stanton

Due to the nature of the web we cannot guarantee the content or links of any site mentioned. We strongly recommend that teachers check websites before using them in the classroom.

Authors
Ann Montague-Smith and Julia Stanton

Commissioning Editor
Paul Naish

Development Editors
Kate Pedlar and Pollyanna Poulter

Editors
Niamh O'Carroll and Rhiannon Findlay

Series Designer
Andrea Lewis

Designer
Ricky Capanni (International Book Management)

Illustrator
International Book Management

Credits & Acknowledgements
© Crown copyright material is reproduced under the terms of the Click Use Licence.

Contents

Introduction to Scholastic Data Handling

About the series

Scholastic Data Handling is designed to support primary teachers by helping their students in using important data-handling skills every day. Each title in the series provides opportunities for using relevant data within all subject areas, as defined by the National Curriculum. By using the series, a teacher or school can be confident that they are embedding data handling, so that children are given real opportunities to find data from sources such as other people, books and the internet, and to use data in a variety of practical ways.

The importance of data handling

Every day we encounter data. This might be through television programmes, internet searches to find the best price for something, comparing costs in shops, and in discussions with others. Children will come across data from very early on, such as how many grapes each of them in a group has, how tall their tower of bricks is compared with those of others, and so on. As children become older and develop their own interests, they will encounter data in areas such as sports and their results, shopping and getting good value for money, or where they might go on holiday.

In order to foster development in data handling, children need to experience using real data, in real-life situations, as often as possible, so that they make the connections between what they learn at school and life outside school. Eventually, when children leave education and begin employment, data-handling skills will be vital to them in managing their work and living in society.

About this book

This book provides full coverage of the Data Handling strand from the Primary National Strategy: *Framework for Teaching Mathematics*.

Each double-page lesson consists of one page with lesson details and a second, photocopiable, activity sheet typically showing a data-handling diagram, chart or graph. Where possible, data-handling software, such as a graphing or pictogram tool, is incorporated into the lesson. Children's own data can be captured using this software, then displayed on the interactive whiteboard for all to see and discuss.

Across the series, each area of the National Curriculum is visited. If a subject area does not lend itself well to realistic data for a certain age range, this has been left for a later book to ensure the data is always pertinent.

Lesson structure

Each lesson contains:

- Mathematics objective(s) for the relevant year group taken from the Primary National Strategy for Mathematics and the National Curriculum. At least one objective from the data-handling strand is included for every lesson. National Curriculum objectives have been abbreviated, but full details can be found on a planning grid in the 'planning' area of the CD-ROM. Subject-specific objective(s) taken from the National Curriculum requirements or guidelines for the subject are also included.
- The vocabulary that specifically relates to the data handling content of the lesson.
- A list of resources, including practical materials, activity sheets that can be displayed or printed and references to images and interactive data-handling tools on the CD-ROM.

> **Resources**
> - Seeds, such as sunflower or runner bean; pots, compost, gardening equipment; uniform non-standard units of length, such as interlocking cubes
>
> **CD-ROM slideshow:**
> - Activity sheets: 'Growing seeds – table' (two copies for each child), 'Growing seeds block graph' (two copies for each child) and 'Sunflower challenge' (also p37)
> - Images: 'Growing sunflower'; 'Growing seeds'
> - Block graph tool

- An introduction to the lesson, including questions to ask the children about the topic and the data.
- The children's task, which may be for group, paired or individual work.
- Differentiation to help you decide how to help the less confident learners in your group or class, and how to extend the learning for the more confident.
- A review of the lesson, where children's work may be considered, or where further data is introduced. This section includes more questions to ask the children in order to identify their level of understanding.
- A 'Now try this…' section, which has further ideas for activities based on the curriculum topic and its data-handling possibilities.
- CD-ROM follow-up material, which consists of images to stimulate enquiry or use of the data-handling tools to extend the investigation.
- An activity sheet with material which may form part of the Introduction, the Children's task or the Review.

How to use the CD-ROM

- The CD-ROM needs to be installed. Double-click the 'installDHYear2.exe' file, and follow the instructions onscreen to install the software to your network or computer. If you or your school has purchased more than one *Scholastic Data Handling* title, these will all feed into the same, single, *Scholastic Data Handling* program.
- The opening menu asks you to choose between a Teacher Zone and a Kids Zone.

Kids Zone

- The Kids Zone comprises eight maths tools to create and print: sorting and Venn diagrams; Carroll diagrams; pictograms; tables and charts; block graphs; bar charts; line graphs and pie charts.

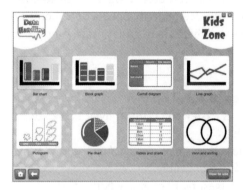

Teacher Zone

- **The Teacher Zone is password-protected. The password is: login.**
- Once in this zone, the relevant year group can be selected, which takes you to a lesson menu. There is at least one ready-made slideshow per lesson that includes all the CD-ROM resources needed: images, activity sheets, ready-made 'interactive' graphs, Word documents and so on.

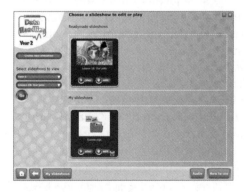

- It is possible to edit or create bespoke slideshows, selecting from all the resources provided for all years that have been installed. It is also possible to upload your own resources into the *Scholastic Data Handling* program. Bespoke slideshows are saved in the 'My slideshows' area.

Slideshow resources across the series include:

- Activity sheets as PDF files that can be printed or displayed, and editable activity sheets in Word or Excel. Images and video which can be displayed on a computer or interactive whiteboard.
- The same tools provided in the Kids Zone, as well as ready-made 'interactives' within slideshows.

A more detailed 'How to use' document is provided on the CD-ROM.

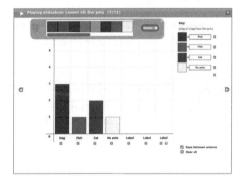

How to integrate data handling within a cross-curricular approach

When data handling is used as part of a topic or investigation, it gives children some insights into how they can use what they know in different curriculum areas, and in real life. The data handling in this series of books evolves naturally from the topics. In this way the children will experience data that is realistic, and relevant to them. Similarly, the 'Now try this...' section of the lessons gives further examples of collecting and using data in real-life situations. Within any topic there will be specific aspects of handling data that fit well within the subject matter. It is much better to use those aspects of handling data where they arise naturally, rather than try to 'force' data from topics.

This book provides opportunities for children to collect data, then organise it. There are opportunities to make tables, diagrams and graphs, as appropriate to the topic. There are also lots of opportunities to ask questions about the data, and to compare the class or individual children's data with that contained in the tables or graphs on the photocopiable pages provided in the book and on the CD-ROM.

◧SCHOLASTIC

Electrical appliances

Mathematics learning objectives
Framework:
- **HD:** Answer a question by collecting and recording data in lists and tables; represent the data as block graphs or pictograms to show results; use ICT to organise and present data.
- **HD:** Use lists, tables and diagrams to sort objects; explain choices using appropriate language, including 'not'.

NC: Ma2, 5a-b

Science learning objectives (NC)
- **Sc4, 1a:** About everyday appliances that use electricity.

Vocabulary
Count, list, sort, table, tally

Resources
CD-ROM slideshow:
- Activity sheets: 'Electrical store' (also p7), 'Electrical appliances table', 'Electrical appliances', 'Electrical store block graph' (also p7) and 'School appliances table'
- Image: 'Kitchen'
- Block graph tool
- Interactive block graph: 'Electrical store'

Introduction
Discuss what things children use at home that need electricity to make them work. Discuss how some things use batteries that can be recharged; others need mains electricity; and that there are other things that do not need any power. Display the image 'Kitchen' from the CD-ROM, if necessary, to prompt discussion. Ask questions such as:
- *What do you have at home that works with batteries?*
- *What do you use that needs mains electricity to work?*
- *Think of some other things that use electrical power.*

If the children have not been introduced to tallying, explain this system. For each item that works with electricity draw a stroke on the board. Put the 'bar gate' across for the fifth item, and so on. Show the children how to count in fives, then add on ones. Display the activity sheet 'Electrical store' and discuss the tally chart.

Children's task
Provide A3 copies of activity sheets 'Electrical appliances table' and 'Electrical appliances'. Ask the children to look at the pictures, and write each item that uses electricity into the correct field on the table. Children may want to write items in more than one row because they have it in two or more rooms, for example, a lamp. Ask: *Are there items which do not use electricity to make them work?* There is space provided for children to add more rooms, such as a garage, study and so on. They tally each item as they place it onto their sheet.

Differentiation
More confident: Challenge the children to think of more items that use electrical power to add to their table.
Less confident: Suggest that the children take each picture in turn, decide whether it works with electricity, write its name onto the table if appropriate, then tick the picture. This will help them to be more methodical in their work.

Review
Ask the children to count up their tallies for each room. Discuss how it is easier to count in fives. Now ask questions, such as:
- *Who has more than three electrical appliances in the bedroom? How many more?*
- *What is the largest number in any bathroom?*

Each time, enter the data for the largest number in the block graph tool in the slideshow. Look at the completed block graph and ask, for example:
- *How many more items are there in the... than in the...?*
- *Which room has most/least items?*
- *What is the number difference between most and least? How did you work that out?*

Display the interactive block graph: 'Electrical store' or the activity sheet. Ask questions, such as:
- *How many more kettles are there than cookers?*
- *How meny fewer DVD players are there then televisions?*
- *How many items are there in total in the store?*

If using the interactive, edit the graph and ask the similar questions again.

Now try this...
Children can collect data for outdoor electrical appliances for homework, then produce block graphs.

CD-ROM follow-up material
In small groups, use activity sheet 'School appliances table' to collect data; then create a block graph using the block graph tool in the Kids Zone of the CD-ROM. Display the completed tables with printouts of the block graphs.

Electrical store

- Look at the tally chart and block graph below.
- Jamie collected information from the local electrical store. The tally chart and block graph show the amount of each item Jamie found.

Name of item	Tallies	Total
kettles	HHH ////	9
cookers	//	2
fridges	HHH ///	8
freezers	HHH //	7
televisions	HHH HHH HHH	15
DVD players	HHH HHH //	12

Electrical store block graph

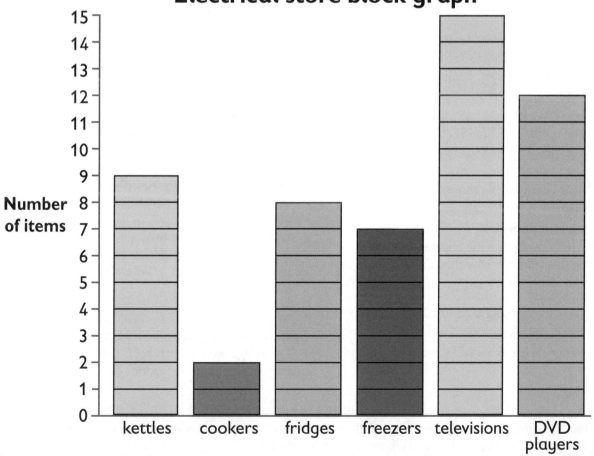

7

How our town has changed

Mathematics learning objectives

Framework:

- **HD:** Answer a question by collecting and recording data in lists and tables; represent the data as block graphs or pictograms to show results; use ICT to organise and present data.
- **HD:** Use lists, tables and diagrams to sort objects; explain choices using appropriate language, including 'not'.

NC: Ma2, 5a-b

History learning objective (NC)

- **4a:** How to find out about the past from a range of sources of information (for example, stories, eye-witness accounts, pictures and photographs, artefacts, historic buildings and visits to museums, galleries and sites, the use of ICT-based sources).

Geography learning objective (NC)

- **3c:** Recognise how places have become the way they are and how they are changing for example, the quality of the environment in a street.

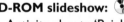

Vocabulary

Block graph, graph, list, table, tally

Resources

- Information resources on the local area (especially shops) now and 100 years ago: for example, large-scale maps, trade directories, books and access to suitable websites

CD-ROM slideshow:

- Activity sheets: 'Brickfield's shops – now' and 'Brickfield's shops – then' (both on p9); and 'Our shops'
- Block graph tool

Introduction

Explain that this lesson may take several days to complete. Discuss how where the children live has changed during their lifetime: new shops, new buildings, and so on. Ask questions such as:

- *What has changed?*
- *Are there new buildings? Where are these?*
- *What else have you noticed?*

Display the activity sheets 'Brickfield's shops – now and

then' and talk about the two block graphs. Check that the children recognise which is 'now' and which is 'then'. Ask questions such as:

- *How many more clothes shops are there than bakers?*
- *How many travel agents and shoe shops are there in total?*
- *How many shops are there altogether?*

Children's task

Put the children into groups of four. Ask some groups to identify what shops there are currently in their village, town or suburb and list these onto the table on activity sheet 'Our shops'. The other groups use the resources you have provided to find out what shops there were in the town 100 years ago. They too collect data using the activity sheet 'Our shops'.

Differentiation

More confident: Encourage the children to make clear lists, and to tally what they find under the headings that they have chosen.

Less confident: The children can list what shops they know from their everyday experiences.

Review

Looking at today's shops, ask how many there are of each type and begin to build a block graph using the block graph tool in the slideshow. Decide on an appropriate scale for the columns, for example, one block represents two shops, and discuss how the amount of data could not easily be shown with one block for one shop. Ask questions such as:

- *How many… are there?*
- *How many more… are there than…?*

Repeat this for the shops of 100 years ago. Provide printouts of both block graphs for the children to compare. Ask, for example:

- *Why are there so many more shops today?*
- *Do you think as many people used to live in our town as do today?*
- *Why do you think that was?*
- *Are there some shops that we do not have today?*
- *Why do you think that is? Where do we buy these things today?*

Now try this...

Children compare what was sold in one type of shop 100 years ago with what is sold there today. They can use the internet and books for research.

CD-ROM follow-up material

Ask groups to collect artefacts (photographs etc) from family and friends showing the town over a period of time. Work with the children to make a simple timeline using the images.

Brickfield's shops – now and then

Now

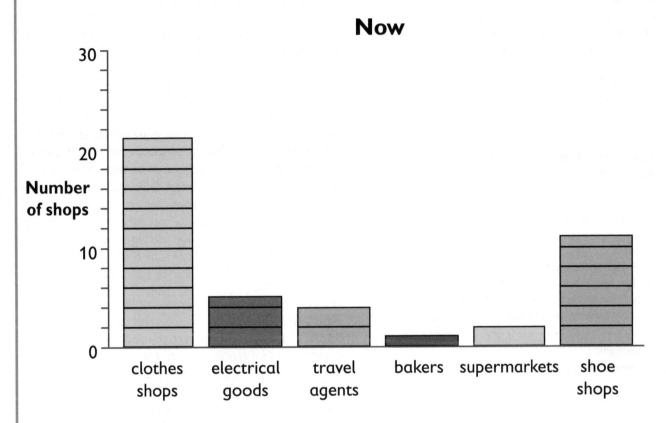

Then

Village life in Uganda

Mathematics learning objectives
Framework:
- **U&A:** Follow a line of enquiry; answer questions by choosing and using suitable equipment and selecting, organising and presenting information in lists, tables and simple diagrams.
- **HD:** Answer a question by collecting and recording data in lists and tables; represent the data as block graphs or pictograms to show results; use ICT to organise and present data.
- **HD:** Use lists, tables and diagrams to sort objects; explain choices using appropriate language, including 'not'.

NC: Ma2, 1a, d-g; 5a-b

Geography learning objectives (NC)
- **2d:** Use secondary sources of information (for example, CD-ROMs, pictures, photographs, stories, information texts, videos, artefacts).
- **3d:** Recognise how places compare with other places (for example, compare the local area with places elsewhere in the United Kingdom).

Vocabulary
Block graph, graph, represent

Resources
- Information resources on the local area, such as books and access to suitable websites

CD-ROM slideshow: 💿
- Activity sheets: 'Village life in Uganda', 'Life in a Dorset village' (also p11) and 'Life in different places', 'Block graph – 1', and 'Block graph – 2'
- Images: 'Ugandan village' 1–4'
- Block graph tool

Introduction
This lesson will probably take more than one day to complete. Display the photographs from the CD-ROM of Ugandan village life and discuss what the children see. Now display and read the activity sheet 'Village life in Uganda'. Discuss the similarities and differences between the lives that the children live and those in Uganda. Ask questions such as:

- *What do you grow in your garden?*
- *Is that the same as in the village in Uganda?*
- *How many different types of shop do you think we have locally?*
- *What about the Ugandan village: how many do they have?*

Look at the bar chart on activity sheet 'Life in a Dorset village' and ask children what they can determine from it. Discuss the questions together.

Children's task
Display the activity sheet 'Village life in Uganda' on the whiteboard and provide copies of activity sheet 'Life in different places'. Ask the children to work in groups of four. They decide what sort of data from the story they will collect, such as the crops that are grown, then find out, using books and the internet, what is grown locally. They complete one table for the Ugandan village, then repeat this for their locality. Using the completed table, each group can create and print a block graph using the block graph tool in the Kids Zone.

Differentiation
More confident: Encourage the children to use the internet to find out more about life in a Ugandan village. They add their findings to their tables.

Less confident: Ask an adult to work with this group. The adult reads the story again, then encourages the children to decide which information they will collect. They can do this as a group activity, using an A3 enlargement of 'Village life in Uganda'.

Review
Decide which of the block graphs to use. Reveal the graph and ask questions such as:
- *How many… are there?*
- *Are there more… or …?*
- *How many fewer… are there than …?*
- *What does one square on the block graph represent? How do you know this?*

Now try this...
- Children find out about life in Kampala, the capital of Uganda, and collect data as above.

CD-ROM follow-up material
Give children, in groups, either activity sheet 'Block graph – 1' or 'Block graph – 2'. Ask them what information they can deduce from their block graph and to think up three or four questions to ask about it. Ask them to say where in the world they think the place might be. If possible make a display of the block graphs and some visual material from the places they represent.

Life in a Dorset village

■ Look at this block graph. It shows the buildings in a village in Dorset.
■ Use the block graph to answer the questions below.

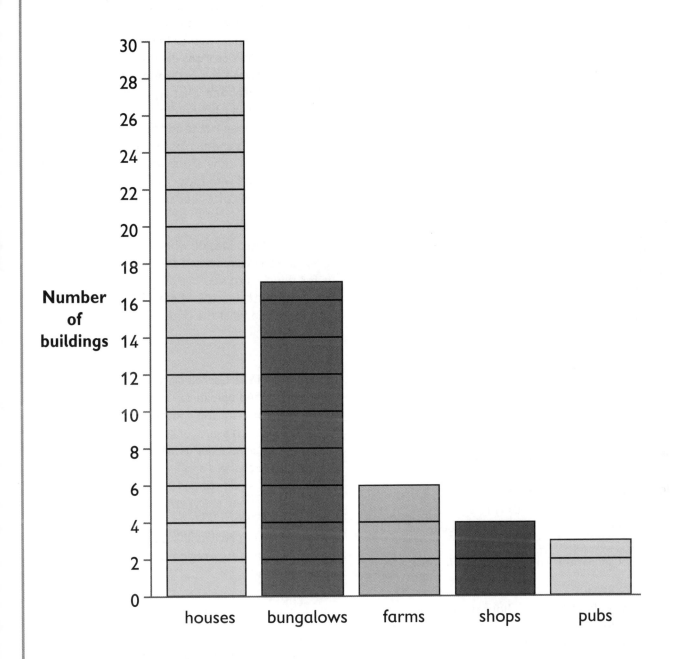

1. How many farms are there?
2. How can you tell?
3. How many bungalows are there?
4. What does one block represent on this graph?
5. What else can you tell?

Victorian houses

Mathematics learning objective
Framework:
- **HD:** Use lists, tables and diagrams to sort objects; explain choices using appropriate language, including 'not'.

NC: Ma2, 5a-b

History learning objective (NC)
- **2b:** Identify differences between ways of life at different times.

Vocabulary
Carroll diagram, different from, least common, list, most common, same as

Resources
- Books and access to the internet for research, digital camera

CD-ROM slideshow:
- Activity sheets: 'Victorian mansion' (also p13), 'Victorian houses table' and 'Victorian house Carroll diagram'
- Images: 'Tudor house' 1–4
- Carroll diagram tool

Introduction
This lesson is likely to take more than one day. Explain to the children that they will be finding out as much as they can about historic houses. You may want to suggest a period in time for them to research, such as Victorian times. Reveal activity sheet 'Victorian mansion'. Ask the children to discuss the image and questions with a partner, if necessary making notes. Then ask:
- *What can you see in the picture?*
- *What do you notice that you don't recognise?*
- *What things are the same as our homes today?*
- *What things are different?*

Make a list of similarities and differences on the board.

Children's task
Provide activity sheet 'Victorian houses table'. In pairs, the children find out as much as they can about Victorian houses, using books and the internet and compare with today. Demonstrate how to make a two-region Carroll diagram, using the tool on the slideshow. Label the first box 'the same as today' and the second one 'not the same as today'. Provide activity sheet 'Victorian house Carroll diagram'. Ask the children to add labels and write or draw to show what goes into each region. Ask them to begin by comparing today's kitchen with a Victorian one. They can consider how people cooked in Victorian times and how we cook today. They can repeat this for how we light our houses now and how the Victorians did this, and then the differences between our bathrooms: how the Victorians washed themselves and what types of toilets they had. They could consider how mothers or their servants cleaned the Victorian house and how this is done today. Washing clothes is another opportunity for comparison. Children may not know about 'washday' and all that this entailed compared with today's washing machines, tumble dryers and clothes that need little or no ironing.

Differentiation
More confident: Decide whether to introduce four-region Carroll diagrams and ask the children to make one for the class to see.

Less confident: Decide whether to work as a group to decide what the criterion should be for the Carroll diagram.

Review
Choose one of the Carroll diagrams, capture it with the digital camera and upload the image for everyone to see. Discuss the criterion chosen, and the data collected. Ask questions such as:
- *What is the same today as in Victorian times?*
- *Have homes changed or are they just the same?*
- *What things would you find in a Victorian home which you would not find today? Why?*
- *What is different?*
- *What else could go onto this Carroll diagram?*

Repeat this with a four-region diagram, if one has been completed.

Now try this...
Children can compare modes of transport between Victorian times and today. They can also compare the clothes that the Victorian children wore with contemporary children's clothes.

CD-ROM follow-up material
Display the photos of Tudor houses from the CD-ROM and ask children to compare them to today's houses (or to the Victorian houses they have been looking at) and make a Carroll diagram to show the differences.

Victorian mansion

- Discuss this Victorian mansion with a partner.
- Now answer the questions.

1. Does this look like your house?
2. What is different?
3. What is the same?
4. How many windows can you see?
5. How many windows does your house have?
6. What sort of chart could we make about this house?

Money

Mathematics learning objectives
Framework:
- **U&A:** Follow a line of enquiry; answer questions by choosing and using suitable equipment and selecting, organising and presenting information in lists, tables and simple diagrams.
- **HD:** Answer a question by collecting and recording data in lists and tables; represent the data as block graphs or pictograms to show results; use ICT to organise and present data.
- **HD:** Use lists, tables and diagrams to sort objects; explain choices using appropriate language, including 'not'.

NC: Ma2, 1a, c–g; 5a–b

Personal, social and health education learning objective (NC)
- **2i:** To realise that money comes from different sources and can be used for different purposes.

· ·

Vocabulary
Count, label, list, table, title

Resources
- Class shop with priced items, toy coins and notes; digital camera

CD-ROM slideshow: 💿
- Activity sheets: 'Price labels', 'Money', 'Blank price labels' and 'Supermarket spend' (also p15).
- Image: 'Shop goods'
- Interactive block graph: 'Supermarket spend'

Introduction
Provide pots of small toy coins and notes for groups and ask the children to put out amounts of money that you say, using the least number of coins and/or notes possible. Encourage the children to discuss their answers in the group, not to put out their first idea. Ask questions such as:
- *How few coins do you need to make 85p?*
- *What about 52p? And 34p?*
- *What about £1.22?*
- *How can you make £1.37? What about £1.53?*
- *Can you find two different ways to make £1.12?*

Children's task
Use activity sheet 'Price labels' to label the items from the class shop. Show the children the items from the class shop with their price labels on. If necessary read all the prices together, to ensure the children are familiar with them. Provide activity sheet 'Money'. Ask the children to choose two items less than £1 and record them on the table. Then ask them to choose another two items for less than £1, and so on until they have chosen nine or ten different combinations of two items.

Differentiation
More confident: Ask the children to choose three items whose total is more than £1.
Less confident: Use activity sheet 'Blank price labels' to write prices suitable for the children's current stage of development. Decide whether to use this, keeping the totals to 20p, for example, for two items.

Review
Photograph some of the completed tables and upload them to the computer. Reveal one of these. Ask questions such as:
- *Look at the pairs of prices. Did you find more? What are they?*
- *Tell me how you found this total. How did you work it out?*
- *Do you think we have found all the possible totals under £1 for two things?*
- *Can you tell that from this table? Why is that?*
- *Repeat for other completed tables.*

Display the activity sheet 'Supermarket spend' and ask the children what they can read from the block graph. Answer the questions together. In small, teacher-led groups they could look at the interactive block graph 'Supermarket spend'; change the amount spent by each child and ask each other questions about the new data.

Now try this...
Children can cut out photos of pets from magazines and create a 'Pet Shop' with prices for each one. Provide a budget, such as £1 or £2. Ask the children to find different combinations of pets from the shop which can be bought for their budget.

CD-ROM follow-up material
Reveal the image 'Shop goods' from the CD-ROM and ask the children to decide how much they think each item would cost in pounds. Ask them to write down their estimate, then check what their partner has written. Challenge them to decide which estimate they think will be closer. Ask for suggestions for each item and choose the most popular each time. Now ask the children to suggest what notes (£5, £10, £20, £50) would be needed to pay for the item. This activity will be a challenge for all of the children.

Supermarket spend

■ This block graph shows how much money five children spent in the supermarket.
■ Look at the block graph and then read the questions below.

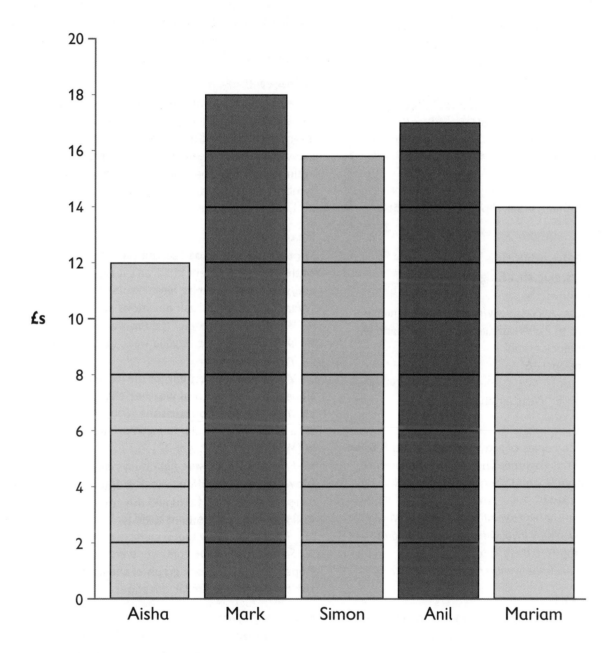

1. How much did Aisha spend?
2. Who spent £6 more than Aisha?
3. How much did Anil spend?
4. How did you work this out?
5. So what does one block stand for?

A Welsh town

Mathematics learning objectives
Framework:
- **U&A:** Follow a line of enquiry; answer questions by choosing and using suitable equipment and selecting, organising and presenting information in lists, tables and simple diagrams.
- **HD:** Answer a question by collecting and recording data in lists and tables; represent the data as block graphs or pictograms to show results; use ICT to organise and present data.

NC: Ma2, 1a, c–g; 5a–b

Geography learning objective (NC)
- **2d:** Use secondary sources of information (for example, CD-ROMs, pictures, photographs, stories, information texts, videos, artefacts).

Vocabulary
Block graph, chart, label, represent, table, title

Resources
- Safety scissors, glue sticks, digital camera

CD-ROM slideshow: 💿
- Activity sheets: 'A Welsh town fact sheet', 'January in Spain' (also p17), 'Weather chart' 1 and 2 and 'A Welsh town block graph'
- Images: 'Location 1–6'
- Block graph tool
- Interactive table: 'Weather chart'

Introduction
Display or provide copies of activity sheet 'A Welsh town fact sheet'. Read this together. Then ask the children to say what they have learned about this town. Ask:
- *Where is the town?*
- *Do you think it is a big town or a small town? Why?*
- *Where could you stay if you went on holiday there?*
- *How many shops are there in total?*
- *What do you think the weather is like in August?*

Children's task
Begin by looking at activity sheet 'January in Spain' and discuss the questions. Then provide the children with activity sheets 'Weather chart' 1 and 2. Ask them to use the information on 'A Welsh town fact sheet' to make a weather chart for the week in August. They cut out the weather symbols and glue them onto the chart.

Next, ask them to choose some of the data from 'A Welsh town fact sheet', such as how many shops or how many places to stay. They then make their own block graph on activity sheet 'A Welsh town block graph', or using the block graph tool in the Kids Zone of the CD-ROM. They write their own title and labels, and decide whether to put a scale of 1:1 or 1:2, depending upon the size of the numbers.

Differentiation
More confident: Challenge the children to find the weather for a week in August where they live from an internet search, and make another weather chart.
Less confident: Read through the information sheet again. Check that the children understand the weather symbols and can match these to the appropriate words in the description of the weather.

Review
Photograph and upload to the class computer one of the more confident children's local weather chart and some block graphs. First, display the interactive 'Weather chart' and ask questions such as:
- *What was the weather like this week?*
- *Do you think it was a good week to be on holiday? Why or why not?*
- *Which was the best day for the weather? Why?*

Repeat this with a local weather chart and ask the children to make comparisons such as:
- *Is the weather similar to the Welsh weather?*
- *Why do you think that is?*
- *How many days were hot/cloudy/rainy?*

Now reveal a completed block graph representing the shops in the Welsh town and ask, for example:
- *What does each square stand for?*
- *How do you know that?*
- *So how many more cafes are there than restaurants?*

Repeat this for a block graph of the accommodation in the town and ask similar questions.

Now try this...
Children make similar charts for their home town and compare for similarities and differences. They collect information in tables.

CD-ROM follow-up material
Display the images 'Location 1–6' from the CD-ROM on the whiteboard (with the captions off) and compare the places. Ask the children, in their groups, to describe each one, including the weather. What categories can they think of to group the images?

January in Spain

■ This chart shows the weather for one week in Spain during January.
■ Look at the chart and then answer the questions.

Saturday	Sunday	Monday	Tuesday	Wednesday	Thursday	Friday

1. How many days were warm?
2. What sort of day was Wednesday?
3. When did it rain?
4. On which two days was it sunniest?

Victorian schools

Mathematics learning objectives
Framework:
- **HD:** Answer a question by collecting and recording data in lists and tables; represent the data as block graphs or pictograms to show results; use ICT to organise and present data.
- **HD:** Use lists, tables and diagrams to sort objects; explain choices using appropriate language, including 'not'.
NC: Ma2, 5a-b

History learning objectives (NC)
- **1b:** Use common words and phrases relating to the passing of time, for example, before, after, a long time ago, past.
- **2b:** Identify differences between ways of life at different times.
- **4b:** To ask and answer questions about the past.

Vocabulary
Block graph, Carroll diagram, label, sort, title

Resources
- Digital camera, access to the internet and books on Victorian times
- **CD-ROM slideshow:**
- Activity sheets: 'Victorian schools', 'Victorian schools Carroll diagram' and 'St Stephen's School in 1885' (also p19)
- Images: 'Victorian school 1–3'
- Block graph tool

Introduction
Display or provide copies of activity sheet 'Victorian schools'. Read it together: you may want to read it through to the children first. Ask the children to think about the Victorian child's experience of school and their own experience. Ask for example:
- *What is the first thing you thought of when we read the information?*
- *What is the same about the Victorian school and school today?*
- *What is different today from the Victorian school?*
- *Can you think of other things which might be different?*
- *Are there more things the same or different?*
- *Which do you prefer? Why?*

Children's task
Display the Victorian school images from the CD-ROM and ask children to discuss them in small groups. Suggest that they make notes that they can use when they move on to the activity sheet. Provide each child with activity sheet 'Victorian schools Carroll diagram'. Ask the children to consider what about the Victorian school is the same as today's school and what is different, referring to their notes if necessary. Ask them to write this onto their Carroll diagram in the correct column. When the children have finished, choose a couple of good examples of Carroll diagrams to share, photograph, and upload onto the class computer.

Differentiation
More confident: Challenge children to find out about other aspects of Victorian school life, for example punishment, toilets and washing facilities, and enter this onto their diagram.

Less confident: Work as a group with an A3 enlargement of the Carroll diagram. Read through the information sheet with the children again. Ask them to pick out the information from each sentence and compare it with today's school.

Review
Display the uploaded completed Carroll diagrams. Ask questions such as:
- *Do you agree with what is in the 'What is the same as school today?' column?*
- *What else could go in that column?*
- *What about the other column? Do you agree?*
- *What do we do in school today that the Victorian children did not?*

Ask the children to make a list of things that are different in today's school from the Victorian school. Then ask them to suggest ideas. Make a class list of the differences. If possible add photographs or drawings of some of the items to the list.

Now try this...
Ask the children to search online and in books for pictures of Victorian schools. Ask them to note what the differences are between the buildings and furniture in Victorian times and today. They can make another Carroll diagram to show this with words or pictures.

CD-ROM follow-up material
Display the activity sheet 'St Stephen's school in 1885' and ask children in small groups to look at the block graph and to answer the questions. Then ask them to find this information for their own school and make their own block graph using the block graph tool in the Kids Zone of the CD-ROM.

Scholastic Data Handling   Year 2

St Stephen's School in 1885

■ This block graph shows information about St Stephen's School in 1885.
■ Look at the graph and then answer the questions.

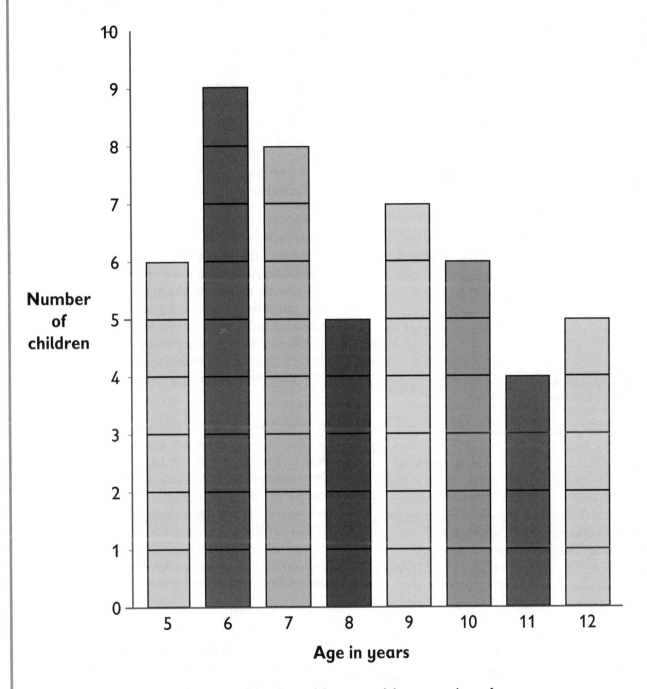

Number of children

Age in years

1. How many more 6-year-olds than 11-year-olds were there?
2. How many children went to St Stephen's school altogether?
3. How many children are there in your Year 2 class?
4. Are there more or less 6- to 7-year-olds in your class than at St Stephen's school?

Celebrations

Mathematics learning objective
Framework:
- **HD:** Use lists, tables and diagrams to sort objects; explain choices using appropriate language, including 'not'.

NC: Ma2, 5a-b

Speaking and listening objective (NC)
- **14:** To listen to others in class, ask relevant questions and follow instructions

Religious education learning objective (NC)
- **1b:** Name and explore a range of celebrations, worship and rituals in religion, noting similarities where appropriate.

Vocabulary
List, sort, table

Resources
- Access to internet and books about religious festivals
- **CD-ROM slideshow:**
- Activity sheets: 'Religious festivals' 1 and 2, 'Celebrations table', 'Christian festivals and celebrations' (also p21) and 'Festivals through the year'
- Table tool
- Word® files: 'Religious festivals' 1 and 2
- Interactive chart: 'Religious festivals'

Introduction
Display activity sheet 'Religious festivals –1' and provide each child with a copy. Read the headings together and check that the children know the names of these religions. Then read through the celebrations under each religion. Explain that these are some of the religious festivals that happen across the world. Ask:
- *Which of these festivals have you heard about?*
- *Do you and your family celebrate any of these festivals?*
- *What can you tell the class about them?*
- *Are any of these festivals similar to ones that we celebrate at school?*

Alternatively, display 'Religious festivals – 2' and ask the children, in groups, to use reference books and the internet to make a class chart of festivals from each of the religions. Word® versions have also been provided so that the charts can be edited.

Children's task
This task may take longer than one lesson. Ask the children to work in small groups of four to six. Each group should choose one or two festivals from 'Religious festivals – 1' or the class chart, for which there is reference material readily available. If necessary, substitute the festivals for content available in your school or library books. The children use the books to find out more about their chosen festivals and how people celebrate them, including clothes, food, and other key features. They record their information on activity sheet 'Celebrations table', the interactive chart 'Religious festivals', or using the table tool in the Kids Zone of the CD-ROM. Ask the children to be ready to talk about the festival(s) that they chose in the review.

Differentiation
More confident: Ask the children to search the internet for further information. With your permission they could print off what they find (copyright permitting) and make these sheets available to the other children in the class.
Less confident: Work as a group. Invite the children to use books and pictures to help them to understand about the festival. They should explain their thinking to the others in their group. Encourage them to make some brief notes about what they find out.

Review
Invite each group to feed back what they have found out about their religious festival. Encourage the children to listen to what each group has to say, then to ask questions. Once each group has fed back, ask questions about the process that they have used, such as:
- *How did you record the information that you found out?*
- *How did it help you to use a table?*

Discuss how using a table can help the children to focus on what they have to do. Explain that data can be collected using words not just numbers.

Now try this...
Reveal activity sheet 'Christian festivals and celebrations' and discuss the questions. The children can use books and the internet to find out more about these religious festivals. Children make a seasons chart of festivals using activity sheet 'Festivals through the year'.

CD-ROM follow-up material
Use the table tool to compile a class chart of festivals from all religions. Print out the table then children can add clip art or illustrations to the chart.

Scholastic Data Handling **Year 2**

Christian festivals and celebrations

■ This table shows Christian festivals and celebrations and when they occur in the year.
■ Read the table and then answer the questions.

Spring	Summer	Autumn	Winter	
Shrove Tuesday	St Swithin's Day	Harvest festival	Advent	
Lent	Lammas	All Saints' Day	Christmas	
Easter			Epiphany	
Mothering Sunday				

1. What happens on Shrove Tuesday?
2. Why is this so important?
3. What is the date for Christmas Day?
4. Is this the same every year?
5. Do you know which festivals and celebrations have different dates each year?

21

Rubbish

Mathematics learning objectives
Framework:
- **U&A:** Follow a line of enquiry; answer questions by choosing and using suitable equipment and selecting, organising and presenting information in lists, tables and simple diagrams.
- **HD:** Answer a question by collecting and recording data in lists and tables; represent the data as block graphs or pictograms to show results; use ICT to organise and present data.
- **HD:** Use lists, tables and diagrams to sort objects; explain choices using appropriate language, including 'not'.

NC: Ma2, 1a, c-g; 5a-b

Science learning objective (NC)
- **Sc2, 5c:** Care for the environment.

Vocabulary
Block graph, graph, label, list, represent, table, tally, title

Resources
- Rubbish from the class bin, sorting rings

CD-ROM slideshow:
- Activity sheets: 'Rubbish', 'Rubbish block graph' and 'Recycling tally charts' 1 and 2 (both on p23)
- Image: 'Recycling crate'
- Block graph tool; table tool
- Interactive charts: 'Jamie's tally chart' and 'Jamilla's tally chart'

Introduction
This lesson takes place across a school week. Reveal the photograph of recycling from the CD-ROM. Discuss what sorts of things families throw away as rubbish and how any rubbish can be recycled. Explain that they will be asked to take turns to sort the rubbish in the class waste bin. Towards the end of the first day, invite two children to empty the bin onto tables and to sort the rubbish into sorting rings. (Check beforehand that there are no sharp or dirty items in the bin, or prepare your own bin in advance.) Ask questions such as:
- *How did you sort this?*
- *How else could it be sorted?*
- *What different things have you found?*
- *Can any of these things be recycled?*

Children's task
Working in pairs, the children begin by adding sorting labels to the activity sheet 'Rubbish'. They then count items and enter the data onto the table on the sheet. Each day ask a different pair or group to sort the rubbish from that day and then repeat the exercise with the rest of the class, so that they can enter the data onto their tables.

At the end of the week provide access to the block graph tool in the Kids Zone of the CD-ROM, or activity sheet 'Rubbish block graph'. Ask some children to complete a block graph for, for example, crisp packets for the week, others for drink cartons, and so on, to cover all the different types of rubbish. Try to ensure that each 'type' of rubbish is completed by someone, even if there is little data.

Differentiation
More confident: Ask the children to make a block graph of one of the items of rubbish where the numbers are larger so that their scale could be 2:1 or 5:1.
Less confident: Choose one of the pieces of rubbish where the number each day is smaller, so that children can use the scale 1:1.

Review
Display one of the block graphs. Ask questions such as:
- *What does one block on the graph represent?*
- *How can you tell that?*
- *On which day was the most… collected?*
- *On which day was the least… collected?*

Reveal other block graphs, and discuss these in a similar way. Now ask:
- *How much of our rubbish could be recycled?*
- *What should we do to try to reduce how much we throw away in this class?*
- *Was there a day when there was no rubbish to be thrown away? Why was this?*

Now try this...
Children can repeat the activity at home. They monitor what is thrown away each day, keep tallied lists, and then produce block graphs of their rubbish.

CD-ROM follow-up material
Display the activity sheet 'Recycling tally charts' or the interactive versions of these on the CD-ROM. Together add the totals for each item. Then ask children to discuss the questions with a partner and note the differences between the two children. Each pair can then create block graphs for one or both of the tally charts using the block graph tool.

Recycling tally charts

- These tally charts show Jamie's and Jamilla's recycling for a week.
- Look at the charts and then answer the questions with your partner.

Jamie's tally chart

Recycling	Tallies	Total
crisp packets	~~////~~ /	
milk cartons	////	
juice cartons	~~////~~ //	
boxes	~~////~~ ///	
newspapers		
pieces of paper	~~////~~ ~~////~~ ~~////~~ ~~////~~ ~~////~~ ~~////~~ ~~////~~ /	
plastic containers	~~////~~ ~~////~~ //	

Jamilla's tally chart

Recycling	Tallies	Total
crisp packets		
milk cartons	~~////~~	
juice cartons	//	
boxes	////	
newspapers	~~////~~ //	
pieces of paper	~~////~~ ~~////~~ ~~////~~	
plastic containers	~~////~~ ~~////~~ ~~////~~ ///	

1. How many crisp packets are in Jamie's chart?
2. How many crisp packets are in Jamilla's chart?
3. How many crisp packets are there in Jamie's and Jamilla's charts in total?
4. Which recycling item has the largest number? Which has the smallest?

Recycling

Mathematics learning objectives
Framework:
- **HD:** Answer a question by collecting and recording data in lists and tables; represent the data as block graphs or pictograms to show results; use ICT to organise and present data.
- **HD:** Use lists, tables and diagrams to sort objects; explain choices using appropriate language, including 'not'.

NC: Ma2, 5a-b

Science learning objective (NC)
- **Sc2, 5c:** Care for the environment.

Vocabulary
Block graph, graph, label, list, pictogram, table, title

Resources
- Digital camera

CD-ROM slideshow: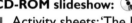
- Activity sheets: 'The James family's recycling' (also p25), 'Recycling list', 'Recycling pictogram' and 'Recycling block graph'
- Images: 'Bottle bank' and 'Recycling bin'
- Pictogram tool; block graph tool

Introduction
Ask the children to think about what things can be recycled at home. Invite suggestions and begin to make a list on the board. After a few suggestions ask: *How can we make this list easier to read?*

Talk about making a list under headings such as 'plastic', 'paper', 'cardboard', 'glass', and so on. Revise the list so that the headings are clear, but do not ask for any more suggestions at this stage. Display activity sheet 'The James family's recycling' and ask the questions.

Children's task
Ask the children to work in groups of four, using the activity sheet 'Recycling list'. Begin by asking the children to make a list of things that they recycle at home. In a class discussion, ask the children for their recycling suggestions; groups can then amend their lists with more headings if necessary. Next, ask the children to work individually. You could direct them to complete either a pictogram or a block graph, or let them decide for themselves. Children can use the activity sheets or the pictogram or block graph tools in the Kids Zone of the CD-ROM to create these. Display in front of the class, as well as a completed 'recycling list'.

Differentiation
More confident: Challenge the children to find at least three more headings.
Less confident: Decide whether to ask an adult to work with this group, using an A3 enlargement of 'Recycling list', so that the children can contribute ideas to the group record. If necessary, choose either the pictogram or block graph and work as a group to move the data from the table onto the graph, with individual children completing a column.

Review
Reveal the uploaded 'Recycling list'. Discuss the additional items added by children to their own lists. Then reveal the pictogram and ask questions such as:
- *What does the pictogram tell you? Is this easy to read?*
- *How many more… are there than…?*
- *How many items are there in total? How did you work that out?*

Repeat this for the block graph using similar questions. Then ask:
- *Which graph did you prefer for this information?*
- *Why did you prefer that one? Explain your thinking.*
  Now ask, for example:
- *Are there things that we would like to recycle but cannot go into the recycling bin?*
- *Where do these things go to be recycled?*

Now try this...
Suggest that the children make a list of local recycling opportunities – paper, plastic, cardboard, and so on. They list places where these things can be recycled.

CD-ROM follow-up material
Use activity sheets 'Recycling list' and 'Recycling pictogram' to investigate school recycling. When children have collected the data ask them to suggest how they could be less wasteful at school. Display the two images 'Bottle bank' and 'Recycling bin' from the CD-ROM, which show recycling schemes from other countries. Ask questions such as: *How do you recycle your aluminium drinks can? What about glass bottles? How do you recycle those? What else can you think of that we should be recycling?*

The James family's recycling

■ This block graph shows the James family's recycling for one week.
■ Look at the graph, then read the questions.

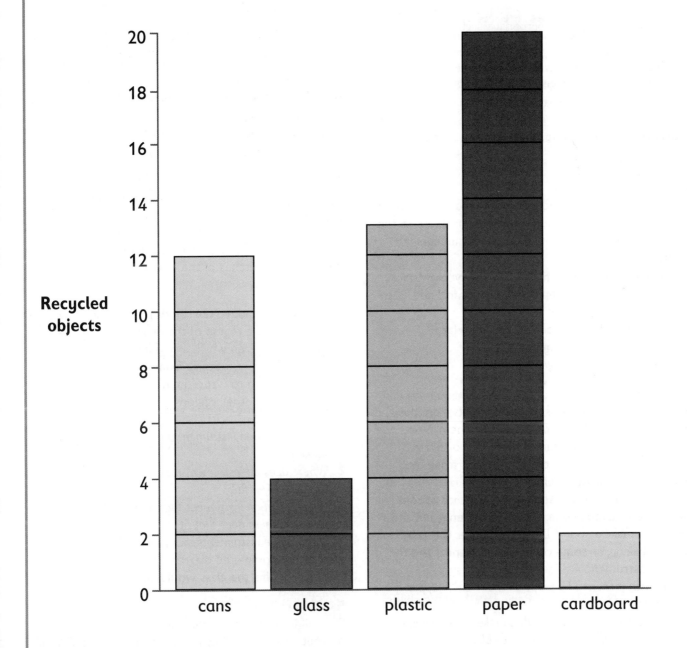

1. How much does one block on this graph represent?
2. How do you know?
3. Which recycling item has the most blocks?
4. Which has the least?
5. How many fewer pieces of cardboard are there than paper?

Sounds

Mathematics learning objective
Framework:
- **HD:** Use lists, tables and diagrams to sort objects; explain choices using appropriate language, including 'not'.

NC: Ma2, 5a-b

Music learning objective (NC)
- **4c:** How sounds can be made in different ways (for example, vocalising, clapping, by musical instruments, in the environment) and described using given and invented signs and symbols.

Vocabulary
Carroll diagram, group, label, list, set, sort, title

Resources
- Musical instruments, including instruments that make their sound by being plucked or blown; access to the internet and books about musical instruments

CD-ROM slideshow:
- Activity sheets: 'Instruments to pluck or blow' (also p27), 'Sounds Carroll diagram', 'Sounds list' and 'Pop music instruments'
- Images: 'Jew's harp', 'Violin', 'Trumpet', 'Harp', 'Glockenspiel' and 'Tambourine'
- Interactive Carroll diagram: 'Sounds'

Introduction
Reveal the photographs of the instruments from the CD-ROM and ask the children to name them. Now reveal activity sheet 'Instruments to pluck or blow', which shows how each of the instruments make their sound. Discuss the questions.

Consider the set of instruments in the classroom. Ask a child to choose one of the instruments and show how it can make a sound. Discuss whether this is by tapping, shaking, or some other means. Repeat this for another instrument. Ask questions such as:
- *This instrument can be tapped. What would happen if we shook it?*
- *Can you find an instrument that makes its sound in a different way from being shaken or blown?*

Display activity sheet 'Sounds Carroll diagram' on the screen and discuss where the instruments would fit on the diagram. Check that the children understand that the bottom-right box is for instruments that make their sound in a way other than being tapped or shaken.

Children's task
Provide copies of activity sheets 'Sounds Carroll diagram' and 'Sounds list'. Ask the children to work in small groups to try out different instruments. They record their findings on 'Sounds list'. When they have tried all of the instruments they put their findings from the list onto the Carroll diagram. It may help the children if there is a list of the instrument names written on the board for them to copy.

Differentiation
More confident: Challenge the children to think of other instruments that they know about, and to include these in their list and Carroll diagram.
Less confident: If the children have some difficulty with writing the words onto the activity sheets, they can quickly make sketches of the instruments.

Review
Display the interactive Carroll diagram 'Sounds' on the screen. Point to a region of the diagram, say top left, and ask the children which instruments would fit into the region. Drag text boxes from the image bank onto the diagram to write the names into the region. Move on to the other regions. Ask:
- *What goes here?*
- *Where would an instrument that can be tapped and shaken go?*
- *Where does an instrument that cannot be tapped but can be shaken fit?*
- *What about an instrument that cannot be tapped or shaken? Where does that fit?*
- *Name some instruments that fit in the bottom-right box.*

Look at the completed diagram together and see if there is anything the class would change.

Now try this...
The children research other instruments, using the internet and books. They make lists and a class Carroll diagram of their findings.

CD-ROM follow-up material
Provide activity sheet 'Pop music instruments' or display it on the whiteboard. Ask the children to work with a partner to think of musical instruments used in pop music and add them to each region of the diagram.

Instruments to pluck or blow

■ This Carroll diagram shows how the instruments in the photographs make sounds.
■ Look at the diagram, then answer the questions.

	Can be plucked	Cannot be plucked
Can be blown	Jew's harp	trumpet
Cannot be blown	violin, harp	tambourine, glockenspiel

1. How does a violin make its sound?
2. What about the trumpet?
3. How does the Jew's harp work?

Buildings

Mathematics learning objectives

Framework:

■ **U&A:** Follow a line of enquiry; answer questions by choosing and using suitable equipment and selecting, organising and presenting information in lists, tables and simple diagrams.

■ **HD:** Use lists, tables and diagrams to sort objects; explain choices using appropriate language, including 'not'.

NC: Ma2, 1a, c–g; 5a–b

Design & technology learning objectives (NC)

■ **1e:** Communicate their ideas using a variety of methods, including drawing and making models.

■ **2d:** Assemble, join and combine materials and components.

· ·

Vocabulary
Carroll diagram, group, list, set, sort, table

Resources

■ Access to an outside area with views of buildings in the locality (optional), materials for constructing houses, such as stiff paper or card; technology kits; digital camera

CD-ROM slideshow: 💿

■ Activity sheets: 'Buildings table', 'Buildings Carroll diagram' and 'Unusual buildings' (also p29)

■ Images: 'Unusual buildings 1–6'

■ Table tool; Carroll diagram tool

Introduction

Decide whether to take the children outside where they can see buildings in the locality. Ask questions such as:

■ *What shapes do you see in the buildings?*

■ *What 3-D shapes can you see?*

■ *What about 2-D shapes?*

Check that the children can discriminate between 2-D and 3-D, for example, a garage is a cuboid, but its door's face has the shape of a rectangle.

Children's task

Ask the children to work in groups of four. They collaborate to construct their own buildings from the materials given. Encourage them to discuss ideas,

then make a quick sketch, and discuss again to refine their ideas. Then they make their buildings. When the buildings are finished, provide access to the table tool and activity sheet 'Buildings table'. The children agree on which shapes they will search for in what they have made, such as cuboids, pyramids, and so on, and they list where these shapes can be found, in their table. When this is completed they enter their data onto activity sheet 'Buildings Carroll diagram', or use the Carroll diagram tool. Remind them that there are two criteria, such as 'Is a cuboid'/'Is not a cuboid' and 'Is a pyramid'/'Is not a pyramid'. Children can draw their shapes onto the Carroll diagram. Ask them to write a title for their diagram. Photograph some of the Carroll diagrams and upload to the class computer, or display completed versions created using the tools.

Differentiation

More confident: Challenge the children to make two tables and Carroll diagrams: one for 3-D shapes and one for 2-D shapes.

Less confident: If children are confused between 3-D and 2-D shapes, only consider one. Ask an adult to work with the children to help them to identify the shapes in their buildings. Decide whether to support them by writing the labels for their criteria onto their Carroll diagram.

Review

Display one of the Carroll diagrams and models. Ask questions, such as:

■ *Which shapes go into the top-/bottom-left space?*

■ *Describe these shapes using the labels.*

■ *Which shapes go into the bottom-right space?*

■ *Describe these shapes using the labels.*

Repeat this for other models and the relevant Carroll diagrams. Discuss how data can be sorted onto Carroll diagrams, and what each space contains, such as top-left space items have both criteria, bottom-right space items have none of the criteria.

Now try this...

Ask the children to find examples of 2-D shapes in their own home, such as flat surfaces (windows, doors, pictures, mirrors…), the circle of the clock face and so on. They use activity sheet 'Buildings Carroll diagram', choosing their own criteria, to record their findings.

CD-ROM follow-up material

Display the photographs of unusual buildings from the CD-ROM. Discuss each building, its key features, and how it is the same as and different from buildings in the children's community. Display activity sheet 'Unusual buildings' and ask the questions about where the buildings have been placed in the diagram.

Scholastic Data Handling **Year 2**

Unusual buildings

■ The photographs of unusual buildings have been sorted into this Carroll diagram.
■ Look at the diagram and then answer the questions.

	Has rectangular faces	Does not have rectangular faces
Has curved walls		
Does not have curved walls		

1. What shapes are in the top-left space?
2. Which buildings do these belong to?
3. What shapes are in the bottom-left space?
4. Which buildings do these belong to?

29

The weather

Mathematics learning objectives
Framework:
- **U&A:** Follow a line of enquiry; answer questions by choosing and using suitable equipment and selecting, organising and presenting information in lists, tables and simple diagrams.
- **HD:** Answer a question by collecting and recording data in lists and tables; represent the data as block graphs or pictograms to show results; use ICT to organise and present data.

NC: Ma2, 1a, c-g; 5a

Geography learning objective (NC)
- **4a:** Make observations about where things are located (for example, a pedestrian crossing near school gates) and about other features in the environment (for example, seasonal changes in weather).

Vocabulary
Block graph, graph, label, list, represent, table, title

Resources
- Thermometers which read from 0°C to 30°C or more, in one degree increments – one for each pair

CD-ROM slideshow: 💿
- Activity sheets: 'Temperatures', 'The weather table' and 'Temperature at East Street School' 1 and 2 (also p31)
- Table tool; block graph tool

Introduction
Introducing the activity on Monday, collect weather data each day and on Friday ask the children to make a block graph of the weather for the week. Choose a week when the temperature outside will be above 0°C. Begin by displaying activity sheet 'Temperatures'. Ask questions such as:
- (Pointing to a thermometer) *What is this called?*
- *What temperature does the first thermometer show?*
- *How did you work that out?*

Repeat this for the other thermometers.

Children's task
Provide activity sheet 'The weather table' or ask the children to use the table tool in the Kids Zone of the CD-ROM. Explain that the children will work in pairs and take turns to take the temperature outside. Back in the classroom, the children record their results on the table. On Friday, with all five days of data, they make a block graph of their results using the block graph tool in the Kids Zone of the CD-ROM. The children will need to decide from their results whether the scale should be in 1s or 2s.

Differentiation
More confident: Ask the children to take another set of readings, this time inside school. Show them how to make a more complex block graph where they record both sets of data for each day alongside each other. Suggest that they do this in two different colours.

Less confident: Work as a group to take the temperatures. Decide whether to write in the scale on the y-axis for the children to make their block graph.

Review
Invite children to say what scale they chose, and why. Ask questions such as:
- *Which is the warmest day? Which is the coolest day?*
- *What is the difference in temperature between the warmest and coolest days?*

Ask the following question of the more confident learners.
- *Was the temperature inside the classroom the same as outside the classroom?*
- *What is the difference in temperature between the inside and outside on Monday?*
- *Which day has the greatest difference in temperature?*
- *What time of year do you think this is?*

Now try this...
Children make a weather chart to show the weather for one week in another place, in the UK or in Europe. They invent their own symbols for sunny, cloudy, and so on.

CD-ROM follow-up material
Reveal activity sheet 'Temperature at East Street School'. Ask questions about each graph in turn, such as:
- *What time of year do you think this is?*
- *What is the difference between the warmest and coolest temperatures?*
- *Which day is cooler than Monday and warmer than Wednesday?*
- *Which was the hottest/coolest day?*
- *What is the difference between the hottest and coolest days?*
- *What sort of weather do you think the children had?*

Temperature at East Street School

■ Look at these block graphs. They show the temperatures for two weeks at East Street School.

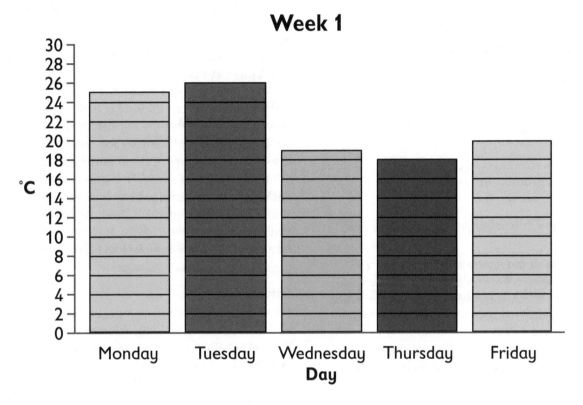

Week 1

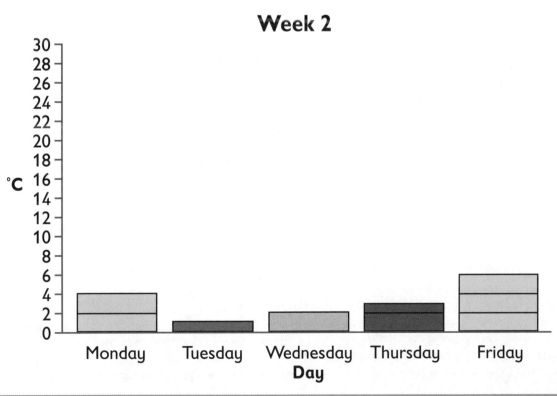

Week 2

Clocks at home

Mathematics learning objective
Framework:
- **HD:** Use lists, tables and diagrams to sort objects; explain choices using appropriate language, including 'not'.

NC: Ma2, 5a-b

History learning objective (NC)
- **4a:** How to find out about the past from a range of sources of information (for example, stories, eye-witness accounts, pictures and photographs, artefacts, historic buildings and visits to museums, galleries and sites, the use of ICT-based sources).

Vocabulary
Analogue, Carroll diagram, different from, digital, least common, list, most common, Roman numerals, same as

Resources
- Books, access to the internet to research clocks through the ages, collection of clocks of different types, such as those with/without Roman numerals, digital clocks, watches, alarm clocks (optional)

CD-ROM slideshow: 💿
- Activity sheets: 'Unusual clocks' (also p33), 'Clocks at home', 'Clocks at home Carroll diagram' and 'Different clocks'
- Images: 'Clocks', 'Church clock', 'Cuckoo clock', 'Clock bells', 'Rolling ball clock' and 'Wall clock'

Introduction
Show the children the collection of clocks. Ask a child to choose one of the clocks and to describe it. Discuss the clock face, what sort of numerals it has, and introduce the terms Roman numerals, digital and analogue if necessary, writing these words on the board. Repeat this for other clocks and watches. If real clocks are unavailable, use the image 'Clocks' from the CD-ROM. Ask questions such as:
- *What sort of clock do you have in your bedroom? Describe it.*

- *Do you wear a watch? Is it digital or analogue?*
- *What other types of clocks or watches do you have at home?*
- *What is the most unusual clock you have at home?*
- *What is the most unusual clock you have seen?*

Then display activity sheet 'Unusual clocks' and discuss how the clocks were sorted in the Carroll diagram.

Children's task
Provide the class with activity sheets 'Clocks at home', and 'Clocks at home Carroll diagram'. Ask the children to work individually to list on the table all the clocks and watches they can think of at home. Alternatively, give children the table the day before the activity and ask them to collect their data for homework. They can draw simple sketches of these as their record. Then ask them to work in pairs. They combine their lists and decide on two criteria, such as 'Is digital'/'Is not digital' and 'Has Roman numerals'/'Does not have Roman numerals'. If necessary, ask for suggestions for criteria from the class. They complete the Carroll diagram using their combined data.

Differentiation
More confident: Challenge the children to complete two Carroll diagrams using different criteria.

Less confident: Work as a group and make a group table, followed by a group Carroll diagram. Encourage the children to describe each timepiece, then to explain why a particular one fits in that space on the Carroll diagram.

Review
Ask children to say what criteria they chose for sorting their combined list. Ask questions such as:
- *What criteria did you use? Why?*
- *What different criteria could you use?*
- *How many of your clocks and watches have this criterion?*

Now try this...
Children search the internet and use books to find examples of unusual clocks or watches. They can sort these using a Carroll diagram as before.

CD-ROM follow-up material
Ask children, in pairs, to find images of a range of clocks in magazines etc., trying to include some unusual ones or using the 'unusual' images from the CD-ROM. They could describe each clock in turn to their partner, and say what is special or different about it. Display activity sheet 'Different clocks' or provide each pair with a copy. Invite children to work out what their criterion should be for sorting their images. Ask them to discuss other methods of sorting.

Unusual clocks

■ How were these clocks sorted?

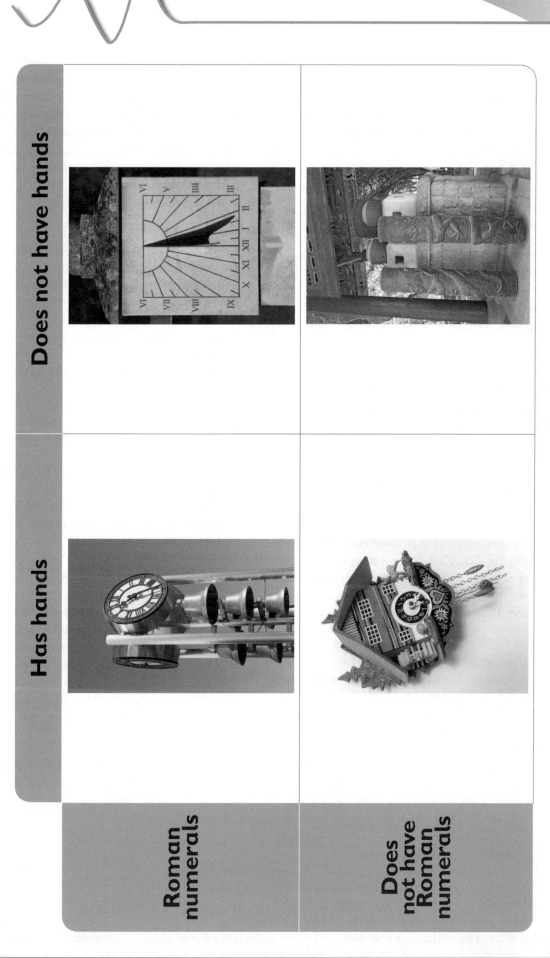

Water clocks

Mathematics learning objective
Framework:
- **HD:** Use lists, tables and diagrams to sort objects; explain choices using appropriate language, including 'not'.

NC: Ma2, 5a-b

History learning objective (NC)
- **4a:** How to find out about the past from a range of sources of information (for example, stories, eye-witness accounts, pictures and photographs, artefacts, historic buildings and visits to museums, galleries and sites, the use of ICT-based sources).

Vocabulary
Block graph, label, represent, table, title

Resources
- Books and access to the internet to research water clocks, plastic bottles with a nail hole in the bottom, access to a sink, paper, glue sticks, minute timers

CD-ROM slideshow: 💿
- Activity sheet: 'Graph of our water clocks' (also p35)
- Images: 'Sand timer', 'Water clock' and 'Sundial'
- Table tool; block graph tool

Introduction
Reveal the images 'Sand timer', 'Water clock' and 'Sundial' from the CD-ROM. Discuss how clocks were made a long time ago. Ask the children if they can think of any other type of clock that does not use hands or digital displays. They may suggest shadow sticks.

Children's task
Explain to the children that their task will be to make a water clock and measure how much the water level drops every minute. Demonstrate how they will make the clocks, using a plastic bottle with a piece of paper stuck down one side so that the water level can be measured. Show them how to fill the bottle to the top of the paper, screw the top back on, then turn it upside down so that the water does not run out. Ask them to work in pairs. They use their minute timer and turn to

the bottle the right way up, over a sink, for a minute. Their partner puts a finger over the hole at the end of the minute, while one of them makes a mark to show where the water level is now. They repeat this for several minutes until the bottle is empty. Now ask the children to work in a group of six to eight. Each group should collect data from their experiment in a table using the table tool, and then make a block graph using the block graph tool in the Kids Zone of the CD-ROM.

Differentiation
More confident: Ask the children to think about why the water level may not appear to go down the same amount each minute. (The bottle may be shaped so that there is more volume of water in the wider parts of the bottle than the narrower parts.)

Less confident: Decide whether to make this a group activity with an adult helping. Ask the adult to help the children to make accurate marks to show where the water level is.

Review
Invite the children to look at each other's water clocks. Ask:
- *Are the marks on the paper all the same distance apart? Why?*
- (Choose a water clock with a shaped bottle) *Why are the marks closer together here than here?*
- *How many minutes does this water clock measure?*

Discuss how different water clocks hold different amounts of water, so they measure different numbers of minutes.

Invite children from each group to show the block graphs that they have made. Ask questions such as:
- *Whose clock lasts for most/least minutes?*
- *How many more minutes does … water clock last than …?*

Reveal activity sheet 'Graph of our water clocks', compare the data with the class data, discuss the differences and answer the questions.

Now try this...
Children use the internet and books to find out more about water clocks, how these were used, and when.

CD-ROM follow-up material
Display the image 'Sundial' from the CD-ROM and ask questions such as:
- *What do you notice about the numbers around the sundial's face?*
- *Where is '12'? How is this different from our clocks?*
- *How is this sundial different from ones we see in gardens today?*

Ask children to find pictures from the library or the internet of sundials over a period of time and note their differences.

Graph of our water clocks

■ This block graph represents how long four children's water clocks lasted.
■ Look at the graph, then read the questions.

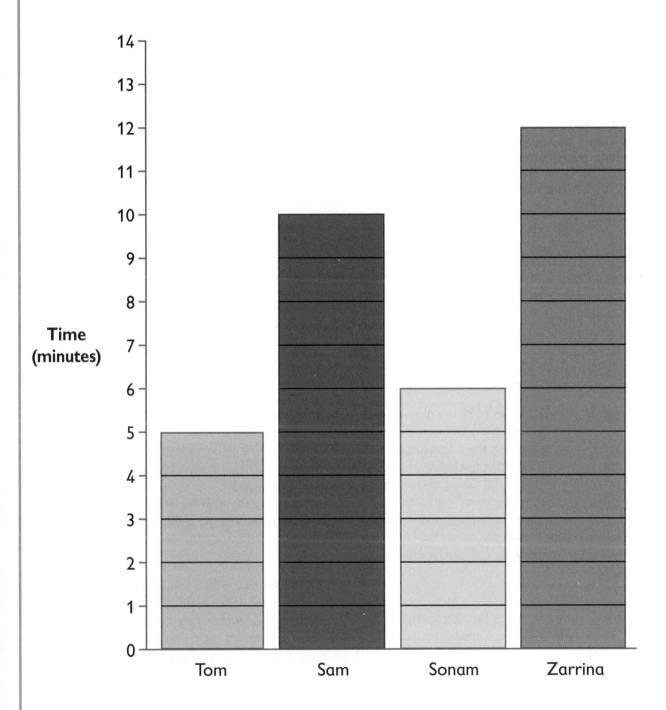

1. Whose clock measures more minutes than Sonam's but fewer than Zarrina's?
2. Why does Zarrina's clock measure more minutes than Tom's?
3. Whose clock measures more minutes than Tom's but fewer than Sam's?

Short tennis skills

Mathematics learning objectives
Framework:
- **U&A:** Follow a line of enquiry; answer questions by choosing and using suitable equipment and selecting, organising and presenting information in lists, tables and simple diagrams.
- **HD:** Answer a question by collecting and recording data in lists and tables; represent the data as block graphs or pictograms to show results; use ICT to organise and present data.

NC: Ma2, 1a, c-g; 5a-b

Physical education learning objective (NC)
- **7c:** Play simple, competitive net, striking/fielding and invasion-type games that they and others have made, using simple tactics for attacking and defending.

Vocabulary
Block graph, list, represent, tally

Resources
- Short tennis racquets, soft balls and short tennis net

CD-ROM slideshow: 💿
- Activity sheets: 'Short tennis table', 'Swallows block graph' (also p37) and 'Panther group'
- Block graph tool

Introduction
This activity can be part of a series of PE lessons where the children play short tennis. With the children's help set up the net for short tennis. Ask them to work in pairs to practise their skills in hitting the ball over the net and returning their partner's ball. Give the children time to improve. Ask questions such as:
- *What have you learned which has helped you to improve?*
- *Show me, without hitting the ball, the stroke that you used.*
- *Is there another way of hitting the ball? (eg forehand or backhand)?*

Children's task
Ask the children to work in threes. Provide activity sheet 'Short tennis table'. Two of the children start a rally. The third child counts the number of times that the ball successfully crosses the net and makes a tally mark on the sheet for each crossing. Once there is an error, such as a child missing the ball, or the ball touching the net and falling to the wrong side, the child who is recording writes the total number of crossings. The children then swap over, until all three have had a turn at recording the results for the others. If time permits have another round of turns.

Differentiation
More confident: Encourage the children to try to keep their rally going as long as possible.
Less confident: If children have difficulty, consider letting them play the same game closer to the net.

Review
Reveal the block graph tool in the slideshow. Explain that the results from each group can be entered onto a class graph. Ask the children to find out the largest number of successful returns over the net. There may be some who have managed more than 20, so discuss whether the scale should be in 1s or 2s. Ask each group to give their three results. Write in initials so that children can see their own results, then enter the numeric result for each child. When the graph is finished ask questions such as:
- *Who had the most number of successful returns over the net?*
- *Which number is the smallest for returns over the net?*
- *What is the difference between these two numbers?*
- *Is the graph easy to read?* (The answer may be 'no' because there is so much data. Discuss how else the data could be shown, such as breaking it into smaller groups.)

Discuss activity sheet 'Swallows block graph' in the same way. Encourage the children to note the scale and how they need to work out two of the results.

Now try this...
Discuss other data which could be recorded, such as how many skips with a rope children can make; how many times they successfully throw and catch a ball. Children can record their data, then work in groups of four pairs to make a block graph.

CD-ROM follow-up material
Display the data sets on activity sheet 'Panther group'. Ask children, with a partner, to use the data to make a block graph using the block graph tool, in the Kids Zone of the CD-ROM, then join with another pair and ask each other questions. Some pairs will be able to make two block graphs.

Swallows block graph

■ Look at this block graph. It represents the throwing and catching by the Swallows team.

■ Now answer the questions.

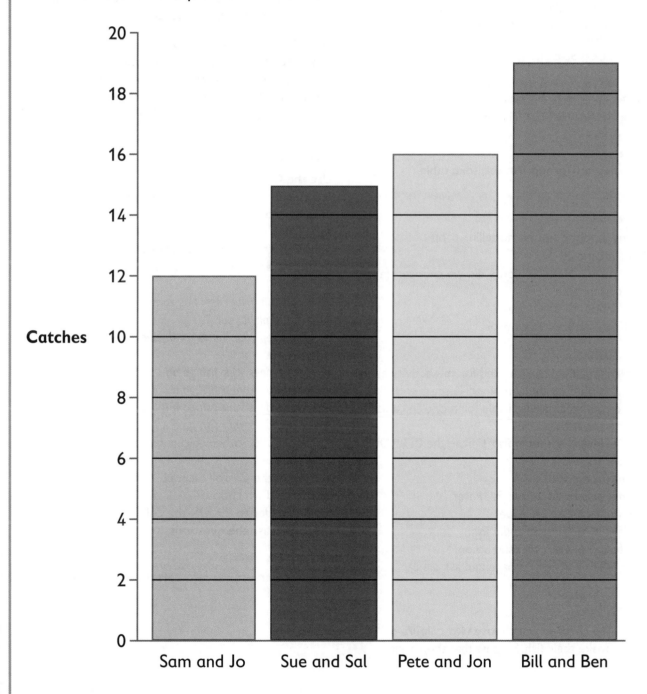

1. How many did partners Bill and Ben score?
2. How do you tell this from the graph?
3. What about partners Sue and Sal's score?

Fish

Mathematics learning objectives
Framework:
- **U&A:** Follow a line of enquiry; answer questions by choosing and using suitable equipment and selecting, organising and presenting information in lists, tables and simple diagrams.
- **HD:** Use lists, tables and diagrams to sort objects; explain choices using appropriate language, including 'not'.
NC: Ma2, 1a, c-g; 5a-b

Art & design learning objective (NC)
- **2b:** Try out tools and techniques and apply these to materials and processes, including drawing.

Vocabulary
Carroll diagram, group, list, set, sort, table

Resources
- Plasticine in four colours, modelling tools
CD-ROM slideshow:
- Activity sheets: 'Which colours did we choose?' (also p39) and 'Fish table'
- Images: 'School of fish' 1 and 2
- Carroll diagram tool; table tool

Introduction
Any modelling medium can be used for this activity as long as two colours can be combined. Discuss with the children the tools that are available for modelling and if necessary demonstrate their use.

Reveal the image 'School of fish 1' from the CD-ROM. Ask questions such as:
- *What colours are the fish?*
- *How many colours does each fish have?*
- *Are the fish all the same shape?*
- *What shapes can you see in the fish?*
- *What about the scales, tail (and so on)?*

Reveal the 'School of fish 2' image and ask similar questions.

Children's task
Explain that the children will choose two colours of plasticine to make their fish. Suggest that they begin by giving some thought to the size of their fish, how it will look and what features it will have. It might help if children sketch their fish on a piece of paper first, showing all the features they would like to include. Their fish should be made up of the two colours used carefully to give an attractive result. They should think about the scales and how they can make those and all the other features using the tools.

Differentiation
More confident: Challenge the children to make more complex fish but still using just two colours of plasticine.
Less confident: Check that the children recognise the main features of fish and that they use their two colours to effect.

Review
Use the Carroll diagram tool in the slideshow to create a four-region Carroll diagram in front of the children. Begin with typing in two colours, such as 'Has red'/'Does not have red', and 'Has blue'/'Does not have blue'. Ask the children to look carefully at their fish and decide where it belongs on the chart. Ask questions such as:
- *Hands up if your fish has some red in it.*
- *Where might your fish go on this chart?*
- *Now keep your hands up if your fish also has some blue in it.*
- *Where does your fish go on the chart?*
- *Where does your fish go if it has red but not blue?*
- *Where does your fish go if it has blue but not red?*
- *Where does your fish go if it has neither red nor blue?*

Repeat this for other colour combinations that the children used.

Reveal the Carroll diagram on activity sheet 'Which colours did we choose?'. Ask the children to look at the table in order to identify the colours that the children used, then ask the questions.

Now try this...
Children can use the two colours of plasticine to model:
- trees,
- boats,
- houses.

CD-ROM follow-up material
Children make fish choosing two colours from blue, red and green only. When their fish are made, they work in groups of six or eight and decide where on activity sheet 'Fish table' their fish belongs. They can make a group table, shading out where the fish cannot fit. Alternatively, they can use the table tool in the Kids Zone on the CD-ROM.

Scholastic Data Handling **Year 2**

Which colours did we choose?

■ Look at this diagram, then answer the questions.

	Brown	**White**	**Green**
Green	Mark	Cathy	
White	Heidi		Sam
Brown		Jon	Peter

1. Why are three spaces in grey?
2. What colours are Cathy's fish?
3. What colour is on Cathy's fish and Sam's fish?
4. Who does not have brown on their fish?
5. Who has a fish that is green and white?

Our pets

Mathematics learning objective
Framework:
- **HD:** Use lists, tables and diagrams to sort objects; explain choices using appropriate language, including 'not'.
NC: Ma2, 5a

Science learning objective (NC)
- **Sc2, 2e:** How to treat animals with care and sensitivity.

. . . .

Vocabulary
Block graph, Carroll diagram, group, list, set, sort, tally

Resources
CD-ROM slideshow:
- Activity sheets: 'Our pets table', 'Our pets block graph', 'Our pets Carroll diagram', 'Class 2A zoo trip' (also p41) and 'Our zoo trip'
- Images: 'Guinea pigs', 'Horse', 'Kitten' and 'Puppies'
- Block graph tool; Carroll diagram tool
- Word® files: 'Our pets table'; 'Our zoo trip'

Introduction
Explain that in this lesson children will be considering the types of pets that they have at home and how these are cared for. Reveal the images of the pets from the CD-ROM. Discuss how pets need to be cared for: they need food, something to drink, somewhere to shelter or sleep, and may need grooming. Discuss this for each of the pet images. Ask the children to make lists of their own pets individually, then in pairs, and finally in groups of eight. If necessary, demonstrate how to use, then count, tally marks. They can use activity sheet 'Our pets table' for this, or the Word® version of 'Our pets table'. Display a completed copy. Invite each group to state what pets they listed and how many. Make a class table. Ask questions such as:
- How many groups of five tally marks are there for dogs?
- How many is that in total?

- Which is the most popular/least popular pet?
- What is the difference in numbers between the most and least popular pet?

Children's task
Ask the children to make a block graph of the number of pets from their group data or from the class data chart, using a scale of one block to two pets. They can use activity sheet 'Our pets block graph' or the block graph tool.

Differentiation
More confident: Ask some of the children to use the block graph tool to make their block graph.
Less confident: Consider limiting the data for these children to that for their own group. They will then be able to use a scale of 1:1.

Review
Display one of the block graphs on screen. Ask questions such as:
- How many does each block stand for?
- How many... are there in total? How many blocks up is that?
- How many more/fewer... than... are there?

Now ask the children to work in pairs. They decide on two criteria for the pets, such as 'Has fur'/'Does not have fur' and 'Eats vegetables'/'Does not eat vegetables'. Using activity sheet 'Our pets Carroll diagram' they write each of the pets into the appropriate place. Use the Carroll diagram tool to create a four-region Carroll diagram. Type in the criteria and invite suggestions for where each pet should go. Ask questions such as:
- Which pets only eat vegetables?
- Which pets do not eat vegetables at all? What do you think these pets eat?
- Which pets have no fur?

Now try this...
Ask the children to think of further criteria by which their pets can be sorted and use the Carroll diagram tool to show this.

CD-ROM follow-up material
Display the activity sheet 'Class 2A zoo trip', discuss the criteria used in the Caroll diagram and the questions with the class. Provide children with activity sheet 'Our zoo trip' or access to the Word® version on the CD-ROM. Each pair should discuss the criteria used by Class 2A, answer the questions, and then add their own criteria to 'Our zoo trip' in pencil, so that they can change them after discussion with another pair. (The criteria are 'Has feathers'/ 'Does not have feathers'; 'Flies'/'Does not fly'.) Ask the groups of four to agree on criteria and answer the questions together.

Scholastic Data Handling   Year 2

Class 2A zoo trip

- This Carroll diagram shows how Class 2A sorted the animals they saw at the zoo.
- Study the diagram with your partner, then answer the questions together.

	Eats leaves	Does not eat leaves
Swims	porcupine	penguin
Does not swim	giraffe	eagle

1. What do you know about these animals?
2. What do they eat?
3. How do they move about?
4. What are they covered with (for example, feathers)?

Holidays

Mathematics learning objectives
Framework:
- **U&A:** Follow a line of enquiry; answer questions by choosing and using suitable equipment and selecting, organising and presenting information in lists, tables and simple diagrams.
- **HD:** Answer a question by collecting and recording data in lists and tables; represent the data as block graphs or pictograms to show results; use ICT to organise and present data.
- **HD:** Use lists, tables and diagrams to sort objects; explain choices using appropriate language, including 'not'.

NC: Ma2, 1a, c-g; 5a-b

Geography learning objectives (NC)
- **3a:** Identify and describe what places are like (for example, in terms of landscape, jobs, weather).

Vocabulary
List, sort, table, vote

Resources
- Digital camera and class computer

CD-ROM slideshow: 💿
- Activity sheets: 'Holidays table' and 'Where are the schools?' (also p43)
- Table tool
- Word® file: 'Holidays table'

Introduction
Ask the children to think about the place that they went to on their last holiday. This can include staying with or visiting family or friends. Ask the children to suggest what they remember about the place that they visited. Ask questions such as:
- *Is there a castle?*
- *Is there a river?*
- *Was the place by the sea?*

Children's task
Ask the children to work individually to make a list of all the things that they remember about their holiday. Provide activity sheet 'Holidays table' or access to the Word® version or table tool on a computer, so that they can see some of the things listed there. Now ask the children to work in groups of up to six. They combine their lists to complete the table. They can add extra categories where necessary. Ask each group to put together a PowerPoint® presentation, or display of photographs from their combined holidays which can be shown to accompany their table.

Differentiation
More confident: Challenge the children to think of five more categories to add to their tables.
Less confident: Decide whether to work as a group. Check that the children understand where to place a tick in a box where their holiday had the particular category. They may need help reading the headings.

Review
Photograph one of the tables, upload to the class computer and display. Ask the children to compare this table with theirs. Ask questions such as:
- *Does Gemma's group have the same things ticked that you did?*
- *Where do you think she went on holiday?*
- *What sort of place was it?*
- *What about Geza's holiday? What sort of place did he go to?*

Point to another child's response on the table. Say:
- *What sort of holiday was this?*
- *How can you tell?*
- *Is this the same as your holiday?*
- *Tell me some differences.*

Display activity sheet 'Where are the schools?' Ask the questions about the schools and describe each of the schools using the information. Discuss how useful the table is in presenting the data.

Now try this...
Ask the children to make a list of things that describe where they live. They combine lists with others and make a group table. They can repeat this for other places, such as where grandparents live. Ask them to bring in photographs and make a display and describe their photographs to a partner.

CD-ROM follow-up material
Make some statements about a place in the UK. After each statement, the children guess where it is. For example:
I am thinking of a large city. It has a castle. It has a palace. It is in England. It has the Houses of Parliament.
Ask children to work in small groups to write statements with which to quiz other groups.

Where are the schools?

- Look at the information in this table. It shows where schools are located.
- Now answer the questions.

School	Town	Country-side	Seaside	River	Shops	Castle
Meadow		✔		✔	✔	✔
St George's	✔			✔	✔	✔
Castle Street	✔		✔	✔	✔	✔
Riverside		✔		✔	✔	✔

1. Which school is by the seaside?
2. How many schools are near a castle?
3. What can you say about Meadow school?
4. What can you say about St George's school?
5. Where is Riverside school?

When our grandparents were children

Resources
- One or two grandparents to come and talk to the children, toys from about 50 years ago

CD-ROM slideshow:
- Activity sheets: 'Jamilla's Grandma's hobbies' and 'Carroll diagram'
- Image: 'Toys'
- Carroll diagram tool

Introduction
Reveal activity sheet 'Jamilla's Grandma's hobbies', and ask the questions. Tell children that a grandparent is coming to visit and ask what they know about their own grandparents' childhoods. Suggest that they talk to their own grandparents, prior to the visit. Invite a grandparent to talk to the children about his or her childhood. Explain to the children that they should listen carefully and then ask questions. Prepare the questions before the visitor arrives. They could ask:
- *How many brothers and sisters did you have?*
- *What toys did you play with?*
- *What games did you play?*
- *Did you have a computerised toy or a computer?*
- *What did you eat? At what time did you go to bed?*

Children's task
Ask the children to make a list of all the things that they remember from the talk. Then the children work with a partner to compare what they have listed. Ask them to choose two criteria, such as 'Had a computer'/'Did not have a computer', and 'Ate pizza'/'Did not eat pizza' and record the grandparent's responses using the activity sheet 'Carroll diagram' or the Carroll diagram tool in the Kids Zone of the CD-ROM. Ask the children to give the Carroll diagram a title and to label the regions.

Differentiation
More confident: Challenge the children to make three different Carroll diagrams from the data that they have collected.
Less confident: Decide whether to ask an adult to work with this group to ask questions to encourage recall of the facts. A group list can be made, with a group Carroll diagram.

Review
Ask individual children to say the criteria that they chose. Now ask the children to suggest some criteria for things that are the same for them as for the grandparent. Make a list of these on the board. Ask questions such as:
- *What foods do you eat that the grandparent also ate?*
- *What toys did the grandparent have that you also play with?*
- *What do you do at school that the grandparent also did?*
- *What time did the grandparent go to bed when they were your age?*
- *Is this the same time as you go to bed?*

Now try this...
Ask the children to find out from grandparents what their interests were when they were children. Back at school, the children can make four-region Carroll diagrams to show some of the hobbies.

CD-ROM follow-up material
Look at the image 'Toys' from the CD-ROM and discuss the toys together. Ask, for example:
- *Which of these things do you do now?*
- *Which of these things would you like to do? Why is that?*
Give children the activity sheet 'Carroll diagram' and ask them to put the items into the diagram using these criteria: 'This toy is electric'/'This toy is not electric' and 'I play with this toy today'/'I do not play with this toy today'.

Scholastic Data Handling   Year 2

Jamilla's Grandma's hobbies

■ Read this list and then answer the questions.

sewing

knitting

embroidery

cooking

reading

looking after my baby sister

skipping outside with my friends

playing ball games outside with my friends

1. Which of these do you do today?
2. What do you do today that is different from these activities?
3. What do you do when you get home from school?

From here to there

Mathematics learning objective
Framework:
- **HD:** Use lists, tables and diagrams to sort objects; explain choices using appropriate language, including 'not'.

NC: Ma2, 5a-b

Design and technology learning objective (NC)
- **2c:** Measure, mark out, cut and shape a range of materials.

ICT learning objective (NC)
- **2c:** How to plan and give instructions to make things happen (for example, programming a floor turtle, placing instructions in the right order).

. . . .

Vocabulary
Label, list, table, title

Resources
- Programmable toy, materials for making roadways, eg long pieces of paper, construction materials

CD-ROM slideshow:
- Activity sheets: 'Akmal's roadway' (also p47), 'From here to there' and 'Roadway cards'

Introduction
This lesson will probably last over several days, with different groups of children taking turns to complete the task. Look together at the programmable toy. Review with the children how to put in instructions for forward, back, and turn. Then ask children to take turns to move the toy. Say, for example:
- *Move forward one. Turn right.*
- *Move back one. Turn left.*

Encourage the other children to check that the instructions programmed are correct.

Display or provide copies of activity sheet 'Akmal's roadway'. Ask a child to try out the instructions with the toy. Ask:
- *What shape has the toy made?*

Children's task
Ask the children to work in groups of up to four. They are to design a roadway and program the toy from the beginning to the end of the roadway route. There should be at least one left or right turn. Ask the children to use activity sheet 'From here to there' to record the shape of their roadway, and then write the instructions for moving the toy from beginning to end. They can make their roadway with long sheets of paper, or mark it out with construction materials. Children may need several copies of the activity sheet before they have completed the task. Their roadway should be displayed together with the finished instruction sheet.

Differentiation
More confident: Challenge the children to put in at least three turns in their roadway to make it more complex.
Less confident: Decide whether to ask the children to make a straight roadway, where the toy leaves the start and crosses the finish with just one forward instruction.

Review
Ask groups to take turns to set up their roadway. Invite others to try out the instructions. Ask questions such as:
- *Did the instructions work well?*
- *Why do you think that was?*

Now choose a more challenging roadway and invite the other children to suggest what the instructions should be (do not show them the instructions at this stage). As the toy is moved, write each instruction on the board so that all the children can see them. When the toy has reached the end of the roadway read out each line of the original instructions. Ask questions such as:
- *Is how we moved the toy the same as the original instructions?*
- *What is different/the same about the instructions?*

Discuss how important it is to write down instructions clearly and accurately so they can be followed.

Now try this...
Ask the children to set up pathways on the playground. These can be marked with chalk lines. Ask the children to think about how they will give clear and careful instructions. They may want to use metre sticks to measure distances. They can use activity sheet 'From here to there' to draw their route and to list the instructions for moving.

Challenge the children to write other instructions for making the toy move in a rectangle, triangle, pentagon, and so on.

CD-ROM follow-up material
Provide each group with activity sheet 'Roadway cards'. Ask them to follow the instructions and to then sketch the roadway indicated by them. Ask them to compare their findings with other groups.

Akmal's roadway

■ These are the instructions Akmal programmed.

Forward 2
Turn right
Forward 2
Turn right
Forward 2
Turn right
Forward 2

■ Draw a sketch of the roadway using the grid below.

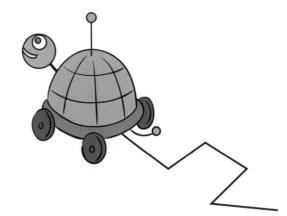

Further ideas

Here are some further ideas for handling data across the curriculum.

Topic	Curriculum area	Handling data
Read poems about characters and record what they are like.	English	Collecting data; making lists.
Children record where their parents were born.	Geography	Collecting data; block graphs of how many parents were born in particular locations.
Research into the school in the past, for example, how many children were in Year 2 ten years ago.	History	Collecting data; block graph using scale of 1:2.
Children listen to several pieces of music and make notes of which they enjoyed.	Music	Collecting data; pictogram of results to show which music was/ was not enjoyed.
Identify and record light sources.	Science	Collecting data and making lists.
List groups that the children belong to, such as family, school, cubs, church and so on.	PSHE	Collecting data, then a table to show who belongs to which groups in the class.
Record weather across the school year.	Geography	Table of what weather patterns occur in each season.
Research using the internet and books the life of a famous person.	History	Collecting data, using lists and tables.
Make a list of rules for the classroom.	PSHE	Collecting ideas, using lists. Producing a finished list which everyone in the class agrees to.